MOVIE TRIVIA

Interactive Quiz

Managing Editors: Simon Melhuish and Sarah Wells

Series Editor: Nikole G Bamford

Designer: Linley J Clode

Writer: Paul Lucas

Cover Design: Alan Shiner

Published by
The Lagoon Group
PO Box 311, KT2 5QW, UK
PO Box 990676, Boston, MA 02199, USA

ISBN: 1904797636

© LAGOON BOOKS 2004

www.intelliquestbooks.com

Printed in China

IntelliQuest

UNIQUE BOOK CODE	007

Instructions

First of all make sure you
have a Quizmo —

Find the book's unique code (this
appears at the top of this page).
Use the ◀ and ▶ buttons to
scroll to this number on the Quizmo
screen. Press the ⬅ button to enter
the code, and you're ready to go.

Use the ◀ ▶ scroll buttons to select
the question number you want to
answer. Press the Ⓐ, Ⓑ, Ⓒ, or Ⓓ
button to enter your chosen answer.

If you are correct the green light beside the
button you pressed will flash. You can then use
the scroll button to move on to another question.

If your answer is incorrect, the red light beside the button
you pressed will flash.

Don't worry, you can try again and again until you have
the correct answer, OR move on to another question.
(Beware: the more times you guess incorrectly, the lower
your final percentage score will be!)

You can finish the quiz at any point — just press
the ⬅ button to find out your score and rank as follows:

75% or above	Outstanding performance! Your knowledge is award-winning!
50% — 74%	You've been nominated for trivia buff of the year.
25% — 49%	Your head for trivia is not in sparkling form.
Less than 25%	Your performance is up for turkey of the year!

If you do press the ⬅ button to find out your score,
this will end your session and you will have to use
the ⬅ to start again!

HAVE FUN!

001

Which of these is the title of a Buster Keaton comedy?

- A The Thickhead
- B The Fathead
- C The Saphead
- D The Slaphead

002

What was the most expensive silent movie ever made?

- A Metropolis
- B Battleship Potemkin
- C Anthony And Cleopatra
- D Ben Hur

003

What famous story was first filmed in 1910?

- A The Wizard Of Oz
- B Hamlet
- C Spartacus
- D Alice In Wonderland

004

What was unusual about the appearance of the silent film star Ben Turpin?

- A He was a hunchback
- B He only had one eye
- C He was a midget
- D He was cross-eyed

Whose voice did we first get to hear in the 1930 film Anna Christie?

005

- A   Bette Davis
- B   Marlene Dietrich
- C   Greta Garbo
- D   Charlie Chaplin

Which of these is credited as being one of the earliest ever Westerns, dating from 1903?

006

- A   The Cabinet Of Dr Caligari
- B   The Thunderers
- C   High Noon
- D   The Great Train Robbery

What was the last silent film to win Best Picture at the Oscars?

007

- A   Metropolis
- B   The Great Dictator
- C   Wings
- D   Ben Hur

– Horror Films –

008 Halloween H20 was dedicated to which actor?

- A Donald Pleasance
- B Peter Cushing
- C Max Schrek
- D Bela Lugosi

009 Which of these notorious horror films was filmed in 3D?

- A Bride of Dracula
- B The Amityville Horror
- C House Of Wax
- D They Came From Outer Space

010 What were "The Triffids?"

- A Alien invaders
- B Zombies
- C Plants
- D Mutant cats

011 Which Horror Movie starred Johnny Depp?

- A Friday the Thirteenth
- B Halloween H20
- C The Burning
- D Nightmare on Elm Street

Who did Wes Craven allegedly name Freddy Krueger after?

012

- **A** A boy who bullied him at school
- **B** His first boss
- **C** The school caretaker
- **D** His father-in-law

Plan 9 From Outer Space, possibly the worst movie ever made, was funded by a Baptist church. What did the cast do in order to secure the funds?

013

- **A** They promised not to swear for the duration of the filming
- **B** They all had to be baptized
- **C** They all had to pay weekly tithes for the rest of their lives
- **D** They promised not to drink alcohol while filming

How tall were the models of King Kong for the 1933 movie?

014

- **A** 10 feet high
- **B** 18 inches high
- **C** 6 feet high
- **D** 4 feet high

015 What was the original title of The Texas Chainsaw Massacre?

A Old Leatherface

B Headcheese

C Slice for Life

D Hope I don't run out of gas!

016 Which horror film did mother and daughter Janet Leigh and Jamie Lee Curtis appear in together?

A The Shining

B Nightmare On Elm Street

C The Watchers

D The Fog

017 What was the first horror movie in color?

A Dracula Meets The Werewolf

B Bride Of Frankenstein

C Horror Of Dracula

D Basketcase

Which Hitchcock film features a Salvador Dali dream sequence?

018

- **A** Spellbound
- **B** Vertigo
- **C** The Birds
- **D** Notorious

What was the 'blood' in the famous shower scene in Psycho made from?

019

- **A** Tomato sauce
- **B** Ox blood and water
- **C** Chocolate syrup
- **D** Milk

Hitchcock made the first British movie with sound in 1929. What was it called?

020

- **A** Rebecca
- **B** Murder!
- **C** Sabotage
- **D** Blackmail

021

The title "North By Northwest" is derived from which play?

A Hamlet

B Macbeth

C Dr Faustus

D The Alchemist

022

Which of these is NOT the title of a Hitchcock film?

A Murder!

B Lifeboat

C Mr & Mrs Smith

D Downstairs

023

What was the name of Hitchcock's first film?

A The Man Who Knew Too Much

B The Lodger

C Jamaica Inn

D Suspicion

024

In which film do we see Hitchcock mail a letter?

A Suspicion

B The Paradine Case

C I Confess

D The Wrong Man

What musical instrument does Hitchcock carry onto a train in Strangers On A Train?

025

- **A** Tambourine
- **B** Trumpet
- **C** Drum
- **D** Double Bass

Hitchcock was reported to have given Tippi Hedren's daughter, Melanie Griffith, a present after The Birds was filmed. What was this gift?

026

- **A** A doll of her mother in a coffin
- **B** A stuffed raven
- **C** A cuddly penguin
- **D** A toy seagull

In which film can Hitchcock be seen tossing some litter outside a theater?

027

- **A** Rear Window
- **B** Easy Virtue
- **C** The 39 Steps
- **D** To Catch A Thief

028 Who was the author of the book upon which Hitchcock's 1936 film Secret Agent was based?

- A W Somerset Maugham
- B Ian Fleming
- C Christopher Isherwood
- D GK Chesterton

029 What does Hitchcock fail to do during the opening credits of North By Northwest?

- A Hail a cab
- B Open an umbrella
- C Buy a newspaper
- D Catch a bus

030 How can you spot Hitchcock in the crowd during the film Frenzy?

- A He's the only one not applauding
- B He's the only one with an umbrella up
- C He's the only one not wearing a hat
- D He's the only one with his back turned

– Screen Stars' Nicknames –

Who was the original "Platinum Blonde?" `031`

- **A** Marilyn Monroe
- **B** Greta Garbo
- **C** Jean Harlow
- **D** Jayne Mansfield

Who was "The Professional Virgin?" `032`

- **A** Doris Day
- **B** Lauren Bacall
- **C** Bette Davis
- **D** Louise Brooks

What was John Wayne's nickname? `033`

- **A** The King
- **B** The Horse
- **C** The Duke
- **D** The Captain

Who was "The Girl With The Million Dollar Legs?" `034`

- **A** Ginger Rogers
- **B** Lana Turner
- **C** Marilyn Monroe
- **D** Betty Grable

035

Dudley Moore was known as "The Sex –?"

- **A** Bomb
- **B** Thimble
- **C** Dwarf
- **D** On Stilts

036

Lana Turner was known as what ?

- **A** The Heels
- **B** The Sweater Girl
- **C** The Silver Fox
- **D** Hotlips

037

What was the nickname of Lauren Bacall?

- **A** The Touch
- **B** The Lady
- **C** The Look
- **D** The Whisper

038

Who was the original "Blonde Bombshell?"

- **A** Marilyn Monroe
- **B** Jean Harlow
- **C** Greta Garbo
- **D** Betty Hutton

– Names and Jobs before they were Famous –

One of Sean Connery's jobs before acting was what? `039`

- A Book editor
- B Coffin polisher
- C Refuse collector
- D TV repair man

What's Richard Gere's middle name? `040`

- A Mouse
- B Purple
- C Tiffany
- D Norman

Which star was born Maurice Micklewhite? `041`

- A Leonardo DiCaprio
- B Cary Grant
- C Michael Caine
- D Peter Cushing

Which star worked in a factory, checking parachutes, before she hit the big time? `042`

- A Joan Crawford
- B Sophia Loren
- C Judy Garland
- D Marilyn Monroe

043

Who once worked as a telephone repair man?

- **A** Clark Gable
- **B** Boris Karloff
- **C** Groucho Marx
- **D** Jack Nicholson

044

Doris Day was once Doris –?

- **A** Von Kapellof
- **B** Smith
- **C** Bubble
- **D** May

045

Who changed their name from William Henry Pratt?

- **A** Bruce Willis
- **B** Peter Cushing
- **C** Eddie Murphy
- **D** Boris Karloff

046

Who won the title of "Miss Hungary" in 1936?

- **A** Zsa Zsa Gabor
- **B** Eva Gabor
- **C** Hedy Lamarr
- **D** Greta Garbo

Susan Weaver changed her name to Sigourney after a character in which book?

047

- **A** A Tale Of Two Cities
- **B** Of Mice And Men
- **C** Black Beauty
- **D** The Great Gatsby

Samuel Goldwyn's real surname was –?

048

- **A** Golden
- **B** Goldfish
- **C** Goldilocks
- **D** Gosburg

Where did Sylvester Stallone used to work?

049

- **A** In a bank
- **B** In a car factory
- **C** In a zoo
- **D** In a garage

Dean Martin used to fight as a boxer under what name?

050

- **A** Marvelous Martin
- **B** Mean Dean Martin
- **C** The Ricochet
- **D** Kid Crochet

051 Judy Garland's original name was Frances what?

- **A** Bumm
- **B** Gumm
- **C** Chumm
- **D** Garland

052 What was the name of the group that later became The Marx Brothers?

- **A** The Six Mascots
- **B** The Four Horsemen
- **C** The Three Ways
- **D** The Five Clucking Chickens

053 What's Charles Bronson's real last name?

- **A** Buchinksy
- **B** Smee
- **C** Bucker
- **D** Bobbit

054 Who fought as a boxer under the name "Packy East?"

- **A** Mickey Rourke
- **B** Clint Eastwood
- **C** Woody Allen
- **D** Bob Hope

What was Rock Hudson's job before he landed acting work?

055

A Pest controller

B Waiter

C Milkman

D Postman

What was Raquel Welch working as before becoming a film star?

056

A A secretary

B A nanny

C A weather girl

D A lawyer

Nicolas Cage changed his surname to stop him being associated with which of his famous uncles?

057

A Steven Spielberg

B Howard Hawks

C Francis Ford Coppola

D David Lean

– Names and Jobs before they were Famous –

058 Who started life as "Roy Scherer?"

- A Rock Hudson
- B James Stewart
- C Stewart Granger
- D Gregory Peck

059 What was Gary Cooper's original first name?

- A Frank
- B Lavender
- C Norbert
- D Minnie

060 What was Bette Davis's original first name?

- A Doris
- B Ruth
- C Gertrude
- D Fanny

061 What's Jack Lemmon's full name?

- A John Uhler Lemmon III
- B Jack Rodney Bickerstaff Lemmon
- C John Capstick-Lemmon
- D Jack Buffalo Lemmon

– Movies for the Young at Heart –

What part did Bert Lahr play in The Wizard Of Oz?

062

- **A** The Wizard Of Oz
- **B** The Scarecrow
- **C** The Tin Man
- **D** The Cowardly Lion

Dumbo sees pink elephants after getting drunk on what?

063

- **A** Moonshine
- **B** Champagne
- **C** Rum
- **D** Fermented apple juice

What was the first X-rated cartoon film?

064

- **A** Felix The Monkey
- **B** Frisky The Lion
- **C** Fritz The Cat
- **D** Freddie and Frank

Which family employed Mary Poppins?

065

- **A** The Banks
- **B** The Walkers
- **C** The Grishams
- **D** The Chimerees

066 What did the Wicked Witch Of The West write in the sky over the Emerald City?

- A Surrender Dorothy
- B Dorothy Go Home
- C I'll Get Toto
- D Oz Is Mine

067 In the film of which famous cartoon strip does the hero battle Big Boy Caprice?

- A Dan Dare
- B Dennis The Menace
- C Dick Tracy
- D Spiderman

068 In The Lady And The Tramp, what food do the dogs eat at Tony's restaurant?

- A Spaghetti
- B Rotten fish
- C Roasted Cat
- D Caviar

What cartoon character did Robin Williams play in the 1980 film?

069

- **A** Tintin
- **B** Popeye
- **C** Dick Tracy
- **D** Captain America

In which film does the Sorcerer Yensid appear ("Disney" spelt backwards)?

070

- **A** The Sorcerer's Apprentice
- **B** Shrek
- **C** Bedknobs And Broomsticks
- **D** Fantasia

In Bambi, some scenes of the forest fire and woodland creatures were unused footage from which movie?

071

- **A** Pinocchio
- **B** Snow White
- **C** Sleeping Beauty
- **D** Cinderella

– Movies for the Young at Heart –

072 What was the first computer-animated feature film?

- **A** Toy Story
- **B** Shrek
- **C** Tron
- **D** Beauty and the Beast

073 In Dick Tracy the colors used for the movie were the original ones used in the comic strip. How many colors were used?

- **A** 32
- **B** 10
- **C** 6
- **D** 2

074 In The Little Mermaid the two-minute storm scene took 10 special effects artists how long to finish?

- **A** 3 months
- **B** 2 years
- **C** 18 months
- **D** 1 year

Who are The Searchers looking for?

075

- A Debbie
- B Eagle Feather
- C Sheriff Pascoe
- D The Man With No Name

What film won Lee Marvin an Oscar for his two roles?

076

- A High Noon
- B Cat Ballou
- C The Good, The Bad And The Ugly
- D Shenandoah

What was John Wayne's last film?

077

- A The Shootist
- B True Grit
- C Unforgiven
- D The Return Of The Rooster

Who played Custer in They Died With Their Boots On?

078

- A James Stewart
- B Errol Flynn
- C Clint Eastwood
- D Mel Brooks

079 Which film is a remake of Akira Kurosawa's Shichinin No Samurai?

- A The Magnificent Seven
- B The Dirty Dozen
- C The Postman
- D The Good, The Bad And The Ugly

080 In what film does the wife of a man who dies during a poker game have to play his hand?

- A The Dead Man's Hand
- B All The Way To The River
- C Aces And Eights
- D Big Hand For A Little Lady

081 Which of these was NOT one of The Magnificent Seven?

- A Lee Marvin
- B James Coburn
- C Horst Bucholz
- D Brad Dexter

Who wrote the film score for Once Upon A Time
In The West?

082

- **A** John Williams
- **B** Ennio Morricone
- **C** Danny Elfman
- **D** John Barry

How many real-life sets of brothers act in The Long Riders,
a film detailing the exploits of the Jesse James gang?

083

- **A** 2
- **B** 5
- **C** 3
- **D** 4

What's the name of the character Clint Eastwood
plays in "Unforgiven?"

084

- **A** John Wilson
- **B** Red Garnett
- **C** William Munny
- **D** Dave Garver

085 **What part did Emilio Estevez play in Young Guns?**

- A Wyatt Earp
- B Butch Cassidy
- C Wild Bill Hickok
- D Billy The Kid

086 **Who was arriving on the midday train in High Noon?**

- A Sheriff Balsberg
- B Mr Peters
- C Jesse James
- D Frank Fuller

087 **Who directed The Outlaw Josey Wales?**

- A Henry Fonda
- B Clint Eastwood
- C Charles Laughton
- D Woody Allen

088 **Which of these films did Charles Bronson NOT act in?**

- A Once Upon A Time In The West
- B The Magnificent Seven
- C Stagecoach
- D Apache

Christopher Lee starred as Scaramanga in The Man with the Golden Gun. His cousin originally wanted him to play Bond. Who was his cousin?

`089`

- **A** Cubby Broccoli
- **B** Roger Moore
- **C** Ian Fleming
- **D** Guy Hamilton

Who sang the theme tune to The Spy Who Loved Me?

`090`

- **A** Shirley Bassey
- **B** Carly Simon
- **C** Sheryl Crow
- **D** Rita Coolidge

Which was the only Bond film to star George Lazenby?

`091`

- **A** Never Say Never Again
- **B** Live And Let Die
- **C** On Her Majesty's Secret Service
- **D** From Russia With Love

092 What was the name of the fictional country that Bond visited in Licence To Kill?

- A San Monique
- B Astrala
- C Marmaville
- D Isthmus

093 The title of which Bond film was suggested by Sean Connery's wife?

- A You Only Live Twice
- B The World Is Not Enough
- C Never Say Never Again
- D Let's Sleep In Separate Rooms From Now On

094 For what Bond film was Louis Armstrong's "We Have All The Time In The World" the theme tune?

- A Thunderball
- B Diamonds Are Forever
- C Dr No
- D On Her Majesty's Secret Service

– Bond Films –

What was the name of M's Russian counterpart?

- **A** Alexis Gogol
- **B** Rudolph Dostoevsky
- **C** X
- **D** Igor Havel

Who played Pussy Galore?

- **A** Maud Adams
- **B** Raquel Welch
- **C** Honor Blackman
- **D** Toyah Brown

Which of these has NOT played "M?"

- **A** Bernard Lee
- **B** Robert Brown
- **C** Judi Dench
- **D** Bob Simmons

Who played "Jaws?"

- **A** Richard Kiel
- **B** Robert Morley
- **C** Raul Morientes
- **D** Sharky Stevens

099 What does "Q's" initial stand for?

- A Quantum
- B Quizzmaster
- C Quatermass
- D Quartermaster

100 What was the name of Bond's wife?

- A Margaret Brown
- B Irma Bunt
- C Contessa Tracy di Vicenza
- D Antonia de Berella

101 What vehicle features prominently in Live And Let Die?

- A A hovercraft
- B A steam train
- C A hot air balloon
- D A double decker bus

102 Which actress was the first to be seduced by Bond?

- A Ursula Andress
- B Lola Fox
- C Eunice Gayson
- D Teri Garr

– Bond Films –

How many Bond films did Timothy Dalton star in?
103

- A Two
- B Four
- C Three
- D One

Who played Tiffany Case in Diamonds Are Forever?
104

- A Lulu
- B Jodie Foster
- C Jill St John
- D Raquel Welch

Which of these actresses has NOT played Moneypenny?
105

- A Lois Maxwell
- B Caroline Bliss
- C Davina Davies
- D Samantha Bond

Who did Bond supposedly work for?
106

- A Acme Financial Services
- B Windsor Consultancy
- C Special Management Ltd
- D Universal Import and Export

107 In which film do we meet the character Christmas Jones?

A The World Is Not Enough

B Diamonds Are Forever

C The Man With The Golden Gun

D Never Say Never Again

108 What was the make of the car that featured prominently in Dr No?

A TR6

B Sunbeam Alpine

C Austin Healey Frogeye Sprite

D Jensen Interceptor

109 In what film does Bond drive a Citroen 2CV?

A Diamonds Are Forever

B For Your Eyes Only

C Thunderball

D On Her Majesty's Secret Service

110 To what organisation does Blofeld belong?

A KGB

B SPECTRE

C UNCLE

D GOBLIN

What was the name of the character played by Ursula Andress in Dr No?

111

- A Helena Backs
- B Moist Bikini
- C Melys Sweet
- D Honey Ryder

What was the name of the operation Bond foiled in Goldfinger?

112

- A Grandma
- B Grandplan
- C Grandslam
- D Grandstand

"Jaws" appears first in The Spy Who Loved Me – in which film does he make a reappearance?

113

- A Moonraker
- B Thunderball
- C The World Is Not Enough
- D The Living Daylights

114 What part did Harold Sakata play in Goldfinger?

- **A** Emilio Largo
- **B** Jaws
- **C** Oddjob
- **D** Blofeld

115 What was the first Bond film to star Roger Moore?

- **A** Dr No
- **B** The Man With The Golden Gun
- **C** The Spy Who Loved Me
- **D** Live And Let Die

116 Which of these does Bond always carry?

- **A** A Ronson lighter
- **B** A monographed handkerchief
- **C** A Cross pen
- **D** An Eton tie

117 Who directed the first Bond film, Dr No?

- **A** Harry Salzman
- **B** Peter R Hunt
- **C** Terrence Malick
- **D** Terence Young

Which country does Bond visit in The World Is Not Enough?

118

A Ukraine

B Azerbaijan

C Japan

D Haiti

What was the name of the villain played by Sean Bean in Goldeneye?

119

A Alec Trevelyan

B Max Strange

C Carlos Rodriquez

D Blofeld

In which of these is Bond NOT played by Pierce Brosnan?

120

A Goldeneye

B The World Is Not Enough

C Tomorrow Never Dies

D Licence to Kill

121 What was the title of Elvis' first film?

- **A** Love Me Tender
- **B** Easy Come, Easy Go
- **C** Girl Happy
- **D** Girls!Girls!Girls!

122 In which Elvis film does his mother appear as an extra?

- **A** Easy Come, Easy Go
- **B** Fun In Acapulco
- **C** Loving You
- **D** Roustabout

123 Which of the films he starred in was Elvis' favorite?

- **A** King Creole
- **B** Love Me Tender
- **C** GI Blues
- **D** Double Trouble

124 What was the name of the Western Elvis appeared in?

- **A** Follow That Dream
- **B** Flaming Star
- **C** Kid Creole
- **D** Charro!

In the film where Elvis plays a doctor, what part does Mary Tyler Moore play?

125

- **A** A nun
- **B** A nurse
- **C** A maid
- **D** A patient

In which of these films is Elvis NOT a racing car driver?

126

- **A** Viva Las Vegas
- **B** Speedway
- **C** Stay Away, Joe
- **D** Spinout

What is Elvis' job in "Paradise Hawaiian Style?"

127

- **A** Helicopter Pilot
- **B** Coastguard
- **C** Fireman
- **D** Race car driver

In which film does Elvis play a riverboat gambler?

128

- **A** Live A Little, Love A Little
- **B** Wild In The Country
- **C** Frankie And Johnny
- **D** Tickle Me

129 What was the name of the character Elvis played in GI Blues?

- **A** Rusty Wells
- **B** Joe Lightcloud
- **C** Jess Wade
- **D** Tulsa McLean

130 What was the name of the troupe of entertainers that Elvis managed in "The Trouble With Girls?"

- **A** The Golden Girls
- **B** The Chautaqua Players
- **C** The Swell Beat Ladies
- **D** The Dixies

131 What was the name of the character Elvis played in Jailhouse Rock?

- **A** Clint Reno
- **B** Vince Everett
- **C** Lucky Jackson
- **D** Deke Rivers

– Birthplaces –

Where was Audrey Hepburn born? 132

- A New York
- B London
- C Brussels
- D Amsterdam

Which of these was NOT born in London? 133

- A Charlie Chaplin
- B Alfred Hitchcock
- C Bob Hope
- D Cary Grant

In which country was Yul Brynner born? 134

- A Great Britain
- B Siberia
- C America
- D Mexico

Which of these actors was born in Beirut? 135

- A Arnold Schwarzenegger
- B Basil Rathbone
- C Keanu Reeves
- D Michael J Fox

136

Where was Billy Wilder born?

- **A** Scotland
- **B** Bulgaria
- **C** Austria-Hungary
- **D** Czechoslavakia

137

Which of these was born in Honolulu?

- **A** Bela Lugosi
- **B** Leonardo DiCaprio
- **C** Holly Hunter
- **D** Bette Midler

138

Which of these was NOT born in Stockholm?

- **A** Ingmar Bergman
- **B** Britt Ekland
- **C** Ingrid Bergman
- **D** Greta Garbo

139

Where was Marlene Dietrich born?

- **A** Berlin
- **B** Liverpool
- **C** Fort Lauderdale
- **D** Paris

The body of which film star was dug up after his death and held to ransom for $600,000?

140

A Buster Keaton

B Groucho Marx

C Fatty Arbuckle

D Charlie Chaplin

What was the name of the prostitute that Hugh Grant procured?

141

A Divine Brown

B Helen Turner

C Fifi Kyle

D Candy Darling

Which of these was jailed for assault on three separate occasions?

142

A Sean Penn

B Mickey Rourke

C Frank Sinatra

D Errol Flynn

143

For what was Sophia Loren once jailed?

A Drunk driving

B Tax evasion

C Prostitution

D Blackmail

144

Which of these was jailed for possessing drugs?

A Sean Connery

B Woody Allen

C Robert Mitchum

D Michael Caine

145

Which film star spent two days in jail after her Broadway show was ruled obscene?

A Bette Midler

B Stockard Channing

C Doris Day

D Mae West

Which of these was caught shoplifting?

146

A Sigourney Weaver
B Winona Ryder
C Joan Crawford
D Courteney Cox

Of what offense was Jane Russell found guilty?

147

A Drunk driving
B Embezzlement
C Actual Bodily Harm
D Spying

Who was arrested for drugs possession, but not charged, in October 1999 when discovered in his house playing bongo drums in the nude?

148

A Matthew McConaughey
B Woody Harrelson
C Christian Slater
D Robert Downey Jr

149 Who or what was "The Pink Panther" in the film?

    A A jewel-thief

    B A car

    C A detective

    D A diamond

150 Which Woody Allen film was subtitled "A Nervous Romance?"

    A The Purple Rose Of Cairo

    B Manhattan

    C Everything You Always Wanted To Know About Sex

    D Annie Hall

151 What was the name of the female character Jack Lemmon plays in Some Like It Hot?

    A Sweetie

    B Carla

    C Daphne

    D Marilyn

In which film are we introduced to The Camberwell Carrot?   152

- **A** My Life As A Dog
- **B** Airplane
- **C** Withnail And I
- **D** The Blues Brothers

What's the name of the character played by Groucho Marx in Duck Soup?   153

- **A** Rufus T Firefly
- **B** Giovanni Amaruso
- **C** Thelonius R Borrower
- **D** Inderwick K Mouserubber

Who turned down the role of Inspector Clouseau, allowing Peter Sellers to step in?   154

- **A** Peter Ustinov
- **B** Spike Milligan
- **C** Dean Martin
- **D** David Niven

– Comedies –

155
Who was the only woman to appear in Dr Strangelove?

A Lily Tomlin

B Tracy Reed

C Katherine Hepburn

D Barbara Streisand

156
What does the traveling salesman played by John Candy sell in Planes, Trains And Automobiles?

A Curtain rings

B Encyclopaedias

C Shoes

D Corsets

157
Who played the King Of The Moon in The Adventures Of Baron Munchausen?

A Eddie Murphy

B Jim Carrey

C Patrick Moore

D Robin Williams

In Three Men And A Baby, which of these was NOT one of the three men?

158

- A Tom Selleck
- B John Goodman
- C Ted Danson
- D Steve Guttenberg

What's the name of the castle full of beautiful women in Monty Python's Life Of Brian?

159

- A Castle NaughtyKnight
- B Lustalot
- C Castle Anthrax
- D Le Chateau Negligé

The only actor in the film M*A*S*H who went on to appear regularly in the TV series played which character?

160

- A Radar
- B Hotlips
- C Hawkeye
- D Fishface

– Comedies –

161 Which of these did not star in the 1980 film 9 To 5?

- A Goldie Hawn
- B Lily Tomlin
- C Jane Fonda
- D Dolly Parton

162 Which star of the James Bond films appeared in Time Bandits, playing Agamemnon?

- A Roger Moore
- B Timothy Dalton
- C Sean Connery
- D Pierce Brosnan

163 When auditioning for Love Happy, which actress obliged when Groucho Marx said there was a role calling for "a young lady who can walk by me in such a manner as to arouse my elderly libido and cause smoke to issue from my ears?"

- A Marilyn Monroe
- B Maureen O'Sullivan
- C Ginger Rogers
- D Thelma Todd

Who played the clerk who receives Dan Aykroyd and John Belushi's money at the end of the film The Blues Brothers?

164

- A Timothy Leary
- B Steven Spielberg
- C Robert Altman
- D David Lean

According to the title of the Steve Martin film, what don't dead men wear?

165

- A Hats
- B Tartan
- C Mauve
- D Plaid

In which film does Cary Grant sit on the gravestone of Archibald Leach, which was his real name?

166

- A Arsenic And Old Lace
- B The Man In The White Suit
- C The Ladykillers
- D The Preacher

167 Who wrote the original screenplay for Rocky?

A Sylvester Stallone

B Stephen King

C Steven Spielberg

D Elmore Leonard

168 The first Sam Spade novel written was turned into which film?

A To Have And Have Not

B The Big Sleep

C The Maltese Falcon

D Film Noir

169 2001: A Space Odyssey was based on which Arthur C Clarke story?

A 2001: A Space Odyssey

B From The Jungle To The Stars

C Whirligig

D The Sentinel

Which famous book was the comedy film Clueless based on?

170

- **A** Emma
- **B** Sense And Sensibility
- **C** Great Expectations
- **D** The Old Curiosity Shop

What film was based on a novel called Red Alert?

171

- **A** Star Wars
- **B** Dr Strangelove
- **C** Deep Impact
- **D** Blade Runner

What was the title of Stephen King's first novel, which was made into a film two years after publication?

172

- **A** Carrie
- **B** It
- **C** Misery
- **D** Stand By Me

173 Which Tarantino film was based on the Elmore Leonard book Rum Punch?

A Reservoir Dogs

B Jackie Brown

C Kill Bill

D Pulp Fiction

174 What famous horror film was based on the book written by William Peter Blatty?

A The Exorcist

B The Amityville Horror

C The Texas Chainsaw Massacre

D Scream

175 What was the name of the Noel Coward play that was later turned into the film Brief Encounter?

A Brief Encounter

B Blithe Spirit

C There's Something In My Eye

D Still Life

– Screenplays and Adaptations –

What film was retitled "Lost Child In Foggy City" in China?

- A Oliver Twist
- B My Life As A Dog
- C Pinocchio
- D Home Alone II

Pierre Boulle wrote the novel that later became which film?

- A Terminator
- B Planet Of The Apes
- C Close Encounters Of The Third Kind
- D The Idiot

Who wrote Lolita?

- A Anton Chekhov
- B Albert Camus
- C Jean-Paul Sartre
- D Vladimir Nabokov

The film Jaws was based on a novel called what?

- A What Lies Beneath
- B The Deep
- C A Stillness In The Water
- D Blood Red Sea

180 Who played the President of the USA in the Tim Burton film Mars Attacks!?

- A Marlon Brando
- B Whoopi Goldberg
- C Martin Sheen
- D Jack Nicholson

181 Blade Runner was adapted from which Philip K. Dick novel?

- A Impostor
- B Valis
- C Flow My Tears, The Policeman Said
- D Do Androids Dream of Electric Sheep?

182 George Lucas took the term Jedi from the Japanese Jidai Geki meaning what?

- A Bad guys
- B Period drama
- C Magical warriors
- D Can you feel the force?

What was under threat in the film Fahrenheit 451?

183

A Water

B Oil

C Books

D Air

In the 1955 film The Quatermass Experiment, a visitor from outer space turns into a blob at which landmark?

184

A The Statue Of Liberty

B The Tower Of London

C Westminster Abbey

D The Pyramids Of Giza

In which film are the characters travelling on the spaceship Nostromo?

185

A 2001:A Space Odyssey

B Alien

C Star Wars

D Spaceballs

186 Who is the first character to speak in Star Wars?

- A Luke Skywalker
- B Darth Vader
- C C-3PO
- D R2-D2

187 What was removed in the director's cut of Blade Runner?

- A All mentions of France
- B The plot
- C Phallic images in some of the background buildings
- D Harrison Ford's narration

188 What was The Man Who Fell To Earth looking for?

- A Gold
- B Uranium
- C Water
- D Omnium

189 In The War of the Worlds what kills off the Martians?

- A An atomic bomb
- B Acid rain
- C Nerve gas
- D The common cold

What was the name of the robot in the 1956 film Forbidden Planet?

190

A Robbie

B Gort

C Sonny

D Marvin

Which of the following wasn't offered the part of Neo in The Matrix?

191

A Ewan McGregor

B Keanu Reeves

C Tom Cruise

D Will Smith

In what film does a spaceship carry the last known examples of earth's flora and fauna?

192

A Galaxy Twelve

B Circlemaker

C Moonfleet

D Silent Running

193

Which film holds the record for the longest list of credits?

- **A** The Matrix Reloaded
- **B** Star Wars
- **C** Alien
- **D** Close Encounters Of The Third Kind

194

Who wrote the book upon which I, Robot was based?

- **A** Philip K. Dick
- **B** Arthur C Clark
- **C** Michael Moorcock
- **D** Isaac Asimov

195

What is faked in Capricorn One?

- **A** An alien invasion
- **B** The election of a black president
- **C** A mission to Mars
- **D** An outbreak of a deadly disease

Which singer starred in the David Cronenberg film Videodrome?

196

- **A** Madonna
- **B** Grace Jones
- **C** Carly Simon
- **D** Deborah Harry

Who made their acting debut in the 1970 film of Joseph Heller's book Catch 22?

197

- **A** Paul Simon
- **B** Stevie Wonder
- **C** Art Garfunkel
- **D** Johnny Cash

Who starred in and sang the theme song to To Sir With Love?

198

- **A** Lulu
- **B** Cilla Black
- **C** Dusty Springfield
- **D** Joni Mitchell

199 In which film would you hear the recurring music "Tara's theme?"

A The Sound Of Music

B Doctor Zhivago

C Gone With The Wind

D ET

200 From which film does the song "Money Makes The World Go Round" come?

A Seven Brides For Seven Brothers

B Grease

C Cabaret

D Mary Poppins

201 Which of these bands did NOT help fund Monty Python's The Holy Grail?

A Pink Floyd

B Led Zeppelin

C Genesis

D The Rolling Stones

John Williams wrote the theme music to which film?   `202`

- A Star Wars
- B The Magnificent Seven
- C The Piano
- D Jaws

What song did HAL sing in 2001: A Space Odyssey?   `203`

- A Danny Boy
- B Daisy, Daisy
- C Happy Birthday
- D John Brown's Body

How many films did The Beatles make?   `204`

- A One
- B Four
- C Two
- D Six

Which film's soundtrack features the music of Dick Dale?   `205`

- A Grease
- B Pulp Fiction
- C Get Shorty
- D True Romance

206 Who directed Moulin Rouge?

- **A** Bruce Beresford
- **B** Jane Campion
- **C** Peter Weir
- **D** Baz Luhrmann

207 Which actress travelled with The Beatles to study at the feet of Maharishi Mahesh Yogi?

- **A** Brigitte Bardot
- **B** Ursula Andress
- **C** Mia Farrow
- **D** Julie Christie

208 The theme song to which James Bond film was written by Paul McCartney?

- **A** Live And Let Die
- **B** The Living Daylights
- **C** Diamonds Are Forever
- **D** Goldfinger

Who turned down the role that made Dustin Hoffman famous in The Graduate?

209

- A Paul Newman
- B Charles Bronson
- C Robert Redford
- D Steve McQueen

What famous part did Gary Cooper turn down the chance to play?

210

- A The Man With No Name
- B James Bond
- C Rooster Cogburn
- D Rhett Butler

What film was Jack Benny due to start shooting just before he died?

211

- A The Sunshine Boys
- B The Towering Inferno
- C Chinatown
- D S•P•Y•S•

212

Who was originally meant to play Ghandi?

- A Robert DeNiro
- B Michael Caine
- C Rock Hudson
- D Anthony Hopkins

213

Who turned down the leading role in From Here To Eternity (for which Deborah Kerr later won an Oscar) on the grounds that she didn't like the costumes?

- A Judy Garland
- B Joan Crawford
- C Jane Russell
- D Greta Garbo

214

George Segal turned down the leading role in which film?

- A 10
- B Tootsie
- C Die Hard
- D Jaws

215

The role that made Eddie Murphy a star in Beverly Hills Cop was turned down by whom?

- A Paul Newman
- B Nicolas Cage
- C Bruce Willis
- D Sylvester Stallone

216

Who wasn't offered the role of Mrs Robinson in The Graduate?

- A Catherine Deneuve
- B Patricia Neal
- C Jeanne Moreau
- D Doris Day

217

James Cameron insisted on Leonardo DiCaprio but who did the studios originally want to play Jack in Titanic (1997)?

- A Tom Cruise
- B Joseph Fiennes
- C Matthew McConaughey
- D Michael Biehn

218

What was Indiana Jones' "real" first name?

A Henry

B Norman

C Spencer

D Ingrid

219

What was the title of Spielberg's first ever feature-length film?

A Jaws

B ET

C Close Encounters Of The Third Kind

D Duel

220

In which film is Spielberg credited as "Steven Spielrock?"

A The Flintstones

B Schindler's List

C Jurassic Park

D Saving Private Ryan

What was the name of Quint's boat in Jaws?

221

- **A** The Blue Lady
- **B** Madeline
- **C** The Orca
- **D** Buster

Spielberg edited Jurassic Park by satellite link whilst he was filming which other feature?

222

- **A** Schindler's List
- **B** Jurassic Park II
- **C** Saving Private Ryan
- **D** The Flintstones

Who wrote the book that Spielberg turned into Jaws?

223

- **A** Stephen King
- **B** James Herbert
- **C** Peter Benchley
- **D** William Burrows

224 Which of these actors did NOT star in How The West Was Won?

  A Gregory Peck

  B John Wayne

  C James Stewart

  D Donald Sutherland

225 Which of these actors did NOT feature in the Robert Altman film Short Cuts?

  A Matthew Modine

  B Tim Robbins

  C Lily Tomlin

  D Tom Waits

226 Which of these did NOT play a part in Love, Actually?

  A Colin Firth

  B George Clooney

  C Hugh Grant

  D Billy Bob Thornton

Which film saw Sean Connery, Ingrid Bergman, Lauren Bacall, Vanessa Redgrave and John Gielgud all star together?

227

A Pret A Porter

B The Princess Bride

C Murder On The Orient Express

D The Adventures Of Baron Munchausen

Which of these wasn't one of The Dirty Dozen?

228

A Telly Savalas

B Charles Bronson

C Lee Marvin

D Clint Eastwood

Which film brought together David Niven, Peter O'Toole, Orson Welles and Woody Allen?

229

A Dirty Rotten Scoundrels

B Casino Royale

C Pret A Porter

D The Princess Bride

230 Who played The Boston Strangler in 1968?

A Jack Lemmon

B Anthony Hopkins

C Tony Curtis

D Peter Cushing

231 Who does Al Pacino team up with to help catch a serial killer in Sea Of Love?

A Marlon Brando

B Paul Newman

C John Goodman

D Brad Pitt

232 Who is Jodie Foster pursuing in The Silence Of The Lambs?

A Hannibal Lecter

B The Bone Man

C Son Of Sam

D Buffalo Bill

What was the first feature film to use the term "serial killer" in its dialogue?

233

- A Cop
- B Manhunter
- C 10 Rillington Place
- D The Silence Of The Lambs

What name was the serial killer in Seven given?

234

- A John Doe
- B The Zodiac Killer
- C The Mothman
- D The Sinner

The serial killer in the film Jennifer 8 specializes in murdering women who are what?

235

- A Pregnant
- B Over 65
- C Overweight
- D Blind

236 Dirty Harry is on the trail of whom?

- **A** Scorpio
- **B** Malthus
- **C** Red Sam
- **D** The Night Stalker

237 Who is the cop in search of a gay serial killer in Cruising?

- **A** Edward G Robinson
- **B** Charles Bronson
- **C** Richard Gere
- **D** Al Pacino

238 On what book by Thomas Harris was the film Manhunter based?

- **A** Hannibal
- **B** Red Dragon
- **C** Hunted
- **D** Food For Thought

Which of these is the title of a film starring Debra Winger as a female serial killer? `239`

- A Man Eater
- B Husband Nine
- C Black Widow
- D Alieen - Portrait Of A Serial Killer

In what film does Sigourney Weaver play an agoraphobic psychiatrist trying to get into the mind of a serial killer? `240`

- A The Silence Of The Lambs
- B Single White Female
- C While You Were Sleeping
- D Copycat

In The Silence Of The Lambs, Hannibal eats the liver of a 'friend' with what accompaniments? `241`

- A Spinach and sake
- B Fava beans and a nice Chianti
- C Haricot Beans and a nice rosé
- D French fries and Coke

242

Name the shortest film ever to win Best Picture at the Oscars?

- A Marty
- B The Way Of All Flesh
- C Ghost
- D Quiz Show

243

What's the name of the lion that roars in the famous MGM logo?

- A Volney
- B Leo
- C Lucas
- D Vinnie

244

What is the name of Charles Foster Kane's estate in Citizen Kane?

- A Brooklands
- B Rosebud
- C Ladyville
- D Xanadu

In which country were The Guns Of Navarone?

245

- A Germany
- B Belgium
- C Greece
- D Turkey

In what film does Stephen King have a cameo role?

246

- A Misery
- B Stand By Me
- C Pet Sematary
- D Carrie

Who starred alongside an ape in Bedtime For Bonzo?

247

- A Bill Clinton
- B George W Bush
- C Ronald Reagan
- D Margaret Thatcher

What was Nicole Kidman's job in To Die For?

248

- A TV Weather Girl
- B Actress
- C Lawyer
- D Waitress

249

What's the name of the script that William Holden tries to sell in Sunset Boulevard?

A Bases Loaded

B Ready For My Close Up

C All About Eve

D Sunset Boulevard

250

What does David Niven pretend to be in the 1975 film Paper Tiger?

A A doctor

B A war hero

C A diplomat

D A nun

251

In which Coen brothers film does John Goodman play a murderer?

A Barton Fink

B The Big Lebowski

C O Brother Where Art Thou?

D Miller's Crossing

What was the name of Liza Minnelli's character in Cabaret?

252

A Sheila Brown

B Samantha Blane

C Suzie Babes

D Sally Bowles

Who played the young Indiana Jones in Indiana Jones And The Last Crusade?

253

A Brad Pitt

B River Phoenix

C Emilio Estevez

D Leonardo DiCaprio

Whose last ever line on screen was "How do you find your way back in the dark?"

254

A Marlene Dietrich

B Greta Garbo

C Marilyn Monroe

D Celia Johnson

255 Sylvia Miles holds the honor of delivering the shortest performance ever to be nominated for an Oscar (six minutes) in which film?

- A Midnight Cowboy
- B Blood Simple
- C Badlands
- D One Flew Over The Cuckoo's Nest

256 Who said "Either this guy's dead or my watch has stopped?"

- A Groucho Marx
- B Woody Allen
- C Humphrey Bogart
- D Steve Martin

257 What language is spoken in Derek Jarman's film Sebastiane?

- A Aramaic
- B Serbo-Croat
- C Latin
- D Urdu

Over 90% of an Oscar statue is made of what?

258

- A Tin
- B Steel
- C Fiberglass
- D Gold

What was the follow-up to The Hustler called?

259

- A The Sting
- B The Color Of Money
- C Cue The Sequel
- D The River Man

Where did the last scene of The Graduate take place?

260

- A By a swimming pool
- B On a pier
- C On an aeroplane
- D On a bus

Who plays Carl Showalter in Fargo?

261

- A Steve Buscemi
- B Peter Stormare
- C Harve Presnell
- D William H Macy

262 What was the last (20th century) Hammer Horror film?

- A To The Devil A Daughter
- B The Hand
- C Forever In The Woods
- D Dracula's Tomb

263 Which actress was Playboy's first ever centerfold?

- A Ursula Andress
- B Jane Russell
- C Marilyn Monroe
- D Tawny Kitaen

264 Who played Sam in Casablanca?

- A Arnold Davies
- B Sidney Walker
- C Bobby Drabble
- D Dooley Wilson

265 In the Truffaut film, who do Jules et Jim both fall for?

- A Catherine
- B Alice
- C Nicole
- D Annabelle

Who is the only actor ever to have won a posthumous Oscar?

266

- A Bruce Lee
- B Peter Finch
- C Brandon Lee
- D River Phoenix

What's the name of the character Dennis Hopper plays in Blue Velvet?

267

- A Frank Booth
- B Paul Abbot
- C Dave Carver
- D Guy Ziles

According to the film title, what age is dangerous for Cynthia?

268

- A 18
- B 30
- C 21
- D 40

269 In what film do we meet "Leatherface?"

A The Texas Chainsaw Massacre

B A Nightmare On Elm Street

C Friday The Thirteenth

D Scream

270 Which comedian is kidnapped in The King Of Comedy?

A Bob Hope

B Archie Bunker

C Woody Allen

D Jerry Lewis

271 At what age did Greta Garbo retire?

A 36

B 29

C 22

D 43

272 Who stars as a policeman in the film The Wicker Man?

A Douglas Raen

B Edward Woodward

C Christopher Lee

D Jack Nicholson

What game features in the film Rounders?

273

- **A** Rounders
- **B** Baseball
- **C** Bare-knuckle boxing
- **D** Poker

Who directed Scanners in 1980?

274

- **A** Steven Spielberg
- **B** John Carpenter
- **C** David Cronenberg
- **D** Wes Craven

What film is being made in Singin' In The Rain?

275

- **A** Pyramus And Thisbee
- **B** Cuckoos In Spring
- **C** The Golden Door
- **D** The Dancing Cavalier

Who appeared as an avant garde artist in the 1990 film Catchfire?

276

- **A** Madonna
- **B** Prince Charles
- **C** Ronnie Biggs
- **D** Bob Dylan

277

Which of these Westerns did NOT win an Oscar for Best Picture?

- **A** Dances With Wolves
- **B** Stagecoach
- **C** Cimarron
- **D** Unforgiven

278

In Singin' In The Rain what did they color the water with to make it show up on screen?

- **A** Shampoo
- **B** Wine
- **C** Milk
- **D** Magnesium salts

279

Who played Tallulah in Bugsy Malone?

- **A** Liza Minnelli
- **B** Melissa Gilbert
- **C** Jodie Foster
- **D** Susan Olsen

Who was billed as "First Irishman" in the film The Long Good Friday?

280

- A Peter O'Toole
- B Pierce Brosnan
- C Bob Hoskins
- D Daniel Day Lewis

Where was the "bridge too far?"

281

- A Italy
- B Germany
- C Holland
- D Norway

Who once said his epitaph should read "He was lucky and he knew it?"

282

- A Brandon Lee
- B Charlie Chaplin
- C Richard Burton
- D Cary Grant

283

What was the name of the film James Dean completed just before he died?

- A Crash
- B Rebel Without A Cause
- C Giant
- D East Of Eden

284

What sort of birds did Dick Van Dyke dance alongside in Mary Poppins?

- A Robins
- B Eagles
- C Parrots
- D Penguins

285

The second-hand coat bought for the character of Professor Marvel in The Wizard Of Oz turned out to have once belonged to whom?

- A L Frank Baum
- B Charlie Chaplin
- C Buster Keaton
- D Judy Garland's grandfather

What's the only film sequel to ever have won Best Picture at The Oscars?

286

A Die Hard With A Vengeance

B The Color Of Money

C The Godfather Part II

D Star Wars: The Phantom Menace

In the film The Good, The Bad and The Ugly who was NOT one of the eponymous three?

287

A Clint Eastwood

B Eli Wallach

C Lee Van Cleef

D Burgess Meredith

In Halloween (1978) Michael Myers' mask was a shop-bought mask painted white. Whose face was on the mask?

288

A Star Trek's Captain James T Kirk

B Porky Pig

C Ronald Reagan

D Elvis

289

Who plays Harry Potter?

- **A** David Renwick
- **B** Rupert Grint
- **C** Dominic Redwood
- **D** Daniel Radcliffe

290

Which film did NOT win the Oscar for Best Picture?

- **A** On the Waterfront
- **B** Marty
- **C** Apollo 13
- **D** The English Patient

291

To date (2004) how many Oscars have been refused?

- **A** 4
- **B** 2
- **C** 1
- **D** 3

292

Which station provided the setting for Brief Encounter?

- **A** Leeds
- **B** Liverpool
- **C** Carnforth
- **D** Coniston

Who was first approached to play Indiana Jones in Raiders of the Lost Ark (1981)?

293

- **A** Tom Selleck
- **B** Harrison Ford
- **C** Richard Dreyfuss
- **D** Don Johnson

Who, aged 14, enrolled in a seminary to become a priest but then dropped out after 12 months?

294

- **A** Leonardo DiCaprio
- **B** Brad Pitt
- **C** Tom Cruise
- **D** John Travolta

To achieve the desired yellow for a field in Lust for Life, the 1956 film about Van Gogh, the director Vincente Minnelli did what?

295

- **A** Planted rapeseed and waited for spring
- **B** Sewed crepe paper onto the existing plants
- **C** Spray-painted the field yellow
- **D** Overexposed the film

296

Jack Nicholson disappeared two months before filming
One Flew over the Cuckoo's nest. Where was he found?

- **A** On a cruising holiday
- **B** He was living in his car
- **C** He had holed up in a bar
- **D** He'd admitted himself into the mental institution
  where the filming took place

297

In When Harry Met Sally who was the woman who
famously said "I'll have what she's having" after Meg
Ryan's faked orgasm.

- **A** Rob Reiner's mother
- **B** Billy Crystal's mother
- **C** Meg Ryan's mother
- **D** Dustin Hoffman dressed up as a woman

298

In what film is the villain a character called Hans Gruber?

- **A** Beverly Hills Cop
- **B** Die Hard
- **C** Diamonds Are Forever
- **D** Conan The Barbarian

In Singin' in the Rain, Debbie Reynolds has to overdub Jean Hagen's singing voice but in reality who dubbed Debbie Reynolds' voice?

299

    A Barbra Streisand

    B Jean Hagen

    C Marni Nixon

    D Carol Channing

What was the first "talkie" — i.e. movie with audible dialogue?

300

    A Blackmail

    B The Jazz Singer

    C Anna Christie

    D The Singing Cavalier

Which 1956 film was the first to feature cameo performances?

301

    A Bus Stop

    B The Wrong Man

    C The Bad Seed

    D Around the World In 80 Days

OTHER TITLES

There are many other exciting quiz
and puzzle books in the IntelliQuest range,
and your QUIZMO electronic unit
knows the answers to them all!

You can order from your
local bookshop or online bookseller.

For a full listing of current titles
(and ISBN numbers) see:

www.intelliquestbooks.com